TRANSFORME

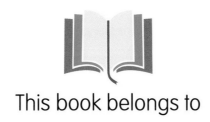

This book belongs to

. . . .

CONTENTS

BRAND NEW **IN HIM**

Paul used to be called Saul. Follow the stepping stones to learn more about him, and to find out why his name changed.

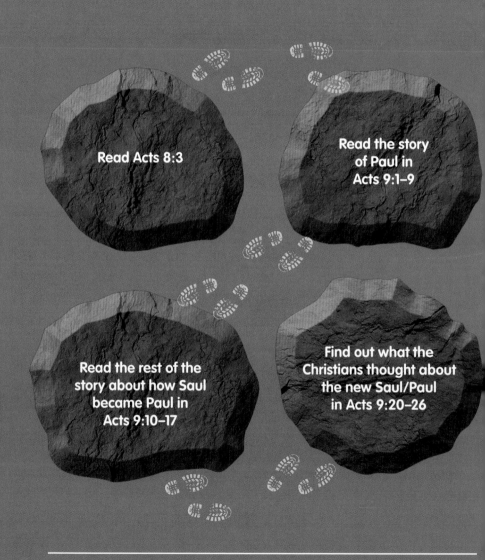

Read Acts 8:3

Read the story of Paul in Acts 9:1–9

Read the rest of the story about how Saul became Paul in Acts 9:10–17

Find out what the Christians thought about the new Saul/Paul in Acts 9:20–26

WHAT DO YOU THINK?

- What do you think Saul was like before he became Paul?

- Saul changed his name to Paul – why do you think this was?

- Saul wasn't very nice to Christians. What do you think they thought when he said he had changed?

- Saul stopped doing some things when he became Paul. Are there any things you want to stop doing?

CREATIVE!

Create a spoon puppet to tell the story of Saul/Paul to your friends. With paint, pens or by sticking things on, make one side happy Paul and the other side grumpy Saul.

PRAY

Think about the amazing transformation that Saul went through when he gave his life to Jesus. You may want to use this prayer to help you pray:

'Dear Jesus, thank You for all you have done for me. Just like Paul I realise I have done things that are wrong. I am sorry for these (tell Jesus the things you are sorry about) and ask You to forgive me. Please help me in the future not to do these things again and to be truly changed, just like Paul. Amen.'

ACTS 8:3
ACTS 9:1–17

FOREVER BLESSED BY HIM

Zacchaeus's life was transformed and blessed by meeting Jesus. Ephesians says that we can be transformed and blessed by Jesus too. Follow the stepping stones to find out more.

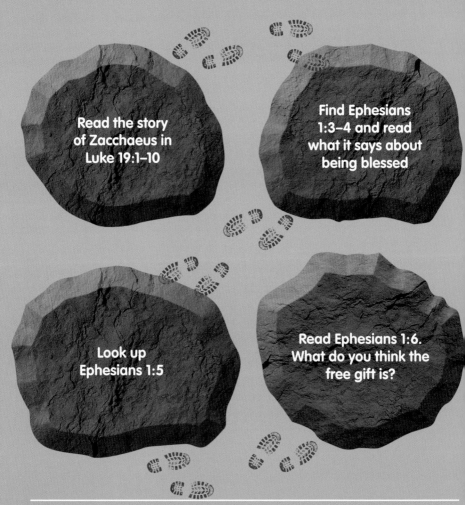

Read the story of Zacchaeus in Luke 19:1–10

Find Ephesians 1:3–4 and read what it says about being blessed

Look up Ephesians 1:5

Read Ephesians 1:6. What do you think the free gift is?

WHAT DO YOU THINK?

- What was Zacchaeus like before he met Jesus?

- How did Zacchaeus change after he met Jesus?

- How do you think he was blessed by Jesus?

- What do you think spiritual blessings are?

- Ephesians 1:5 says that we are children of God. What do you think this means and how does it make you feel?

CREATIVE!
Draw a picture of Zacchaeus giving back the money he owes. Show what you think his face would look like.

PRAY
When Zacchaeus said sorry to Jesus, he became a son of God, just like it says in Ephesians. You might like to pray this prayer, thanking God for all He has done:

'Dear God, I want to thank You that You chose me before the world began, to be Your child. I want to thank You that because of Jesus I can be holy and clean when You look at me. I want to thank You that as Your child I can be set free from all my sins. Amen.'

LUKE 19:1–10

PRAY TO KNOW
HIM BETTER

Martha loved Jesus a lot and wanted things to be perfect for Him when He came to her house. Her sister Mary, however, did not see things like Martha. Follow the stepping stones to find out more.

Read the story of Martha and Mary in Luke 10:38–42

Read Ephesians 1:16. Paul gives thanks for the love the Ephesian believers have for God

Read Ephesians 1:18. We too need to ask Jesus to help us understand more about Him

What does Ephesians 1:19–20 have to say about the strength of the power that God places in us?

WHAT DO YOU THINK?

- Who do you mostly behave like – Mary or Martha? Why?

- Why do you think Jesus thought it was more important for Mary to listen to Him than it was for Martha to serve Him?

- Do you listen to Jesus? When do you think is the best time to listen to Jesus?

- Where do you think is the best place to listen to Jesus?

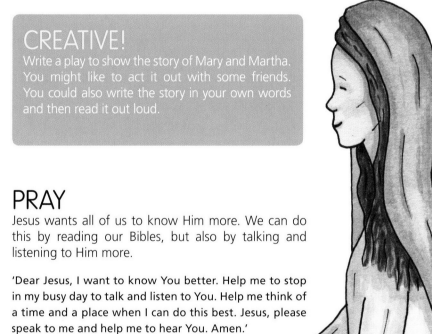

CREATIVE!
Write a play to show the story of Mary and Martha. You might like to act it out with some friends. You could also write the story in your own words and then read it out loud.

PRAY
Jesus wants all of us to know Him more. We can do this by reading our Bibles, but also by talking and listening to Him more.

'Dear Jesus, I want to know You better. Help me to stop in my busy day to talk and listen to You. Help me think of a time and a place when I can do this best. Jesus, please speak to me and help me to hear You. Amen.'

LUKE 10:38–42

ALIVE FOR **HIS PURPOSE**

Can you imagine not being able to be with your family because you were so ill? The ten men with leprosy were not allowed to be with their friends or family because the illness was so easy to catch. Follow the stepping stones to find out more.

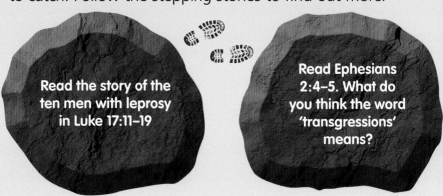

Read the story of the ten men with leprosy in Luke 17:11–19

Read Ephesians 2:4–5. What do you think the word 'transgressions' means?

```
R P B H K S E C T T N B S K
F R X R L N H E F L K Z I R
Y I Y S I C Z O N S T T C D
T E D N A L X G U O U F K Q
E S L N K M V P I T Y S N P
N T X J R G A P L H J U E J
D S L I F E H R D E O P S J
X N P T J T M E I Y P Z S G
B H M W A N D L K A H E H X
N B T E L A J N L G L E R M
N B D I E C A C Q M X V A S
Q W Q R A H W L D K G J N L
N V D G T F N G A L I L E E
P Q Z H T D I S T A N C E N
```

Find the words in the search:

- DEATH
- DISTANCE
- DREADED
- FAITH
- GALILEE
- HEAL
- JESUS
- LEPERS
- LIFE
- NINE
- ONE
- PITY
- PRIESTS
- SAMARIA
- SHOULD
- SICKNESS
- TEN
- THANK YOU

WHAT DO YOU THINK?

- What difference do you think being healed made to the ten men?

- If you were healed in this way what would be the first thing you would do?

- What do you think about the way the nine men treated Jesus after He healed them?

- Ephesians 2:4–5 talks about being 'spiritually dead' – what do you think that means?

- Ephesians also says that it's by 'God's grace' we have been saved. What do you think this means? You might like to look up the word 'grace' in the dictionary to help you.

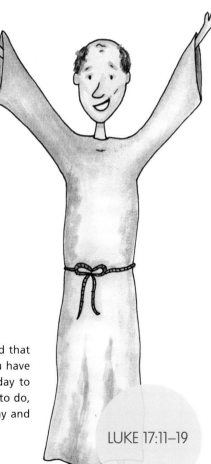

CREATIVE!
Have a go at the word search on the left

PRAY
'Dear Jesus, thank You that You died for me and that You have a plan for my life. Thank You that You have saved me for a purpose and that I am alive today to fulfil this purpose. Show me what You want me to do, Jesus. Show me how to live my life for You today and every day. Amen.'

LUKE 17:11–19

BELONG TO **HIS FAMILY**

Everyone can belong to the family of God. Jesus said that everyone who believed in Him could be called a child of God. The Bible says that all believers are part of God's family. Follow the stepping stones to find out more.

Read about the first Christians in Acts 2:42–47

Read John 1:12. What does it say about everyone who believes in Jesus?

What does Ephesians 2:19 say about us being part of God's family?

Read Galatians 4:6–7. What does this passage say about people who have Jesus in their lives?

WHAT DO YOU THINK?

- Make a list of good things about belonging to a family.

- God says that He is our Father. What do you know about God that makes Him the best Dad ever?

- If Jesus is God's Son and God says we are His children, then that makes Jesus our Brother! How might having Jesus as your big Brother help you?

CREATIVE!
Draw out your family tree – how many people are in your family? Ask other people in your family to help you add in family members from other generations.

PRAY
God wants us all to be part of His family. Jesus died on the cross and rose again so that we could be part of God's family. You might like to pray this prayer:

'Dear Jesus, I want to be part of God's family. I am sorry for all the things I've done wrong. Please forgive me. Jesus, please come into my life and be with me forever. Amen.'

ACTS 2:42–47

GIFTED TO SERVE HIM

God has given us all gifts and talents that make us special. He wants us to use the gifts He has given us to serve Him. Follow the stepping stones to find out more.

Paul says that God gave him a special gift. Read Ephesians 3:7–12 to find out what the special gift was

Read the story Jesus told about three servants in Matthew 25:14–30

In this story, one of the servants didn't use the money he had wisely. What message do you think Jesus was trying to give to the people who were listening to the story?

Read 1 Corinthians 12:4–11 to find out about some of the gifts that God wants to give us

WHAT DO YOU THINK?

- Write down all the special talents you have. You might be good at maths, spelling, singing or dancing. Think about what you're good at.

- We all have things we are naturally good at, but sometimes God wants to give us special new gifts. What gift would you like God to give you? Look at the passage in Corinthians to help you.

- If God gave you a special new gift, how would you use it to serve Him?

CREATIVE!

Make a gift to give to someone. Try to use one of the special talents God has given you to make the gift. If you can sing, write a song and sing it to the person. Write a poem, tell a story, make a practical gift, bake a cake. Ask God to help you think of what you could do.

PRAY

God has given us all gifts to use for Him. You might like to ask God to give you a new gift. Use the prayer below to help you and fill in the gaps as you pray:

'Dear God, thank You for giving me gifts to use to serve You. Help me to use my gifts for good. I would really like the gift of .... and I would like to use this gift to serve You by .... Amen.'

MATTHEW 25:14–30

PRAY TO EXPERIENCE **HIM**

When Jesus healed Bartimaeus so that he could see, Bartimaeus knew that he had met the real Jesus. Jesus wants you to know Him too. Follow the stepping stones to find out more.

Read the story about Bartimaeus in Mark 10:46–52

Read Ephesians 3:16–18. This is a prayer that Paul writes.

WHAT DO YOU THINK?

- Blindfold yourself for a few minutes and see what it's like not to be able to see. How do you feel when you take off your blindfold?

- Jesus gave Bartimaeus a gift even more precious than his sight. What do you think that gift was?

- Would you like to experience Jesus more in your life?

- Do you have anything you would like Jesus to heal you from? Why not ask Him just like Bartimaeus did?

CREATIVE!

Use your very best colouring to colour the picture on the left. When Bartimaeus was blind he couldn't see any colours, but when he could see, it was amazing!

PRAY

You might like to pray this prayer based on Paul's prayer in Ephesians 3:16–18, asking God to help you understand:

'Dear God, please put Your power inside me so that I can understand just how big and deep Your love is for me. Help me to know Your love so that I can become more and more like You every day. Amen.'

MARK
10:46–52

15

A NOTE FOR PARENTS

We hope that you and your child find this book helpful over the next seven weeks, as you go on the Transformed Life journey. To help your child understand the words of Paul in Ephesians, each session has been illustrated with a character or story from the Bible.

We would like to encourage you to support your child with this material. They may need help with finding the passages in the Bible, reading the text and completing the creative elements.

May you find this time with your child a real blessing, as you seek to guide them in their understanding of what a transformed life looks like.

Copyright © 2015 KingsGate
Published 2015 by CWR, Waverley Abbey House, Waverley Lane, Farnham, Surrey GU9 8EP, UK.
CWR is a Registered Charity – Number 294387 and a Limited Company registered in England – Registration Number 1990308.
The right of KingsGate to be identified as the author of this work has been asserted by them in accordance with the Copyright, Designs and Patents Act 1988; sections 77 and 78.
All rights reserved. No part of this publication may be reproduced, stored in a retrieval system, or transmitted, in any form or by any means, electronic, mechanical, photocopying, recording or otherwise, without the prior permission in writing of CWR.
For a list of National Distributors visit www.cwr.org.uk/distributors
Unless otherwise indicated, all Scripture references are from the Holy Bible, New International Version Anglicised (NIV) Copyright © 1979, 1984, 2011 by Biblica (formerly International Bible Society). Used by permission of Hodder & Stoughton Publishers, an Hachette UK company. All rights reserved. 'NIV' is a registered trademark of Biblica (formerly International Bible Society). UK trademark number 1448790.
Concept development, editing, design and production by KingsGate and CWR
Cover image: CWR and OneDollarPhotoClub/ Jag_cz
Printed in the UK by Linney Group
ISBN: 978-1-78259-441-3